© 2008 by Faber Music Ltd
First published by Faber Music Ltd in 2008
3 Queen Square, London WC1N 3AU

Arranged & Engraved by Noam Lederman
Edited by Lucy Holliday & Alex Davis

Guitar by Tom Fleming
Bass by Neil Williams
Drums by Noam Lederman
Mixed & Engineered by Phil Hilborne

Noam is endorsed by
Mapex, Paiste & Protection Racket

Designed by Lydia Merrills-Ashcroft
Photographs © Referns Music Library

Printed in England by Caligraving Ltd
The text paper used in this publication is a
virgin fibre product that is manufactured in
the UK to ISO 14001 standards. The wood
fibre used is only sourced from managed
forests using sustainable forestry principles.
This paper is 100% recyclable

ISBN10: 0-571-53165-2
EAN13: 978-0-571-53165-3
To buy Faber Music publications or to find
out about the full range of titles available,
please contact your local music retailer or
Faber Music sales enquiries:

Faber Music Ltd, Burnt Mill, Elizabeth Way,
Harlow, CM20 2HX England
Tel: +44(0)1279 82 89 82
Fax: +44(0)1279 82 89 83
sales@fabermusic.com fabermusic.com

ON THE CD: FIRST VERSION OF SONG IS THE FULL DEMONSTRATION TRACK, THE SECOND VERSION IS THE BACKING TRACK TO PLAY ALONG TO

I CAN SEE FOR MILES

Words and Music by Pete Townshend

6

miles,_____ oh yeah._____

3. You took ad-van-tage of my trust in you when I was so far a-way.__

I saw you hold-ing lots of oth-er guys and now you've got the

nerve to say:__ that you still want me,__ well that's as may be, but you

got-ta stand trial be-cause all__ the while... I can see for

10

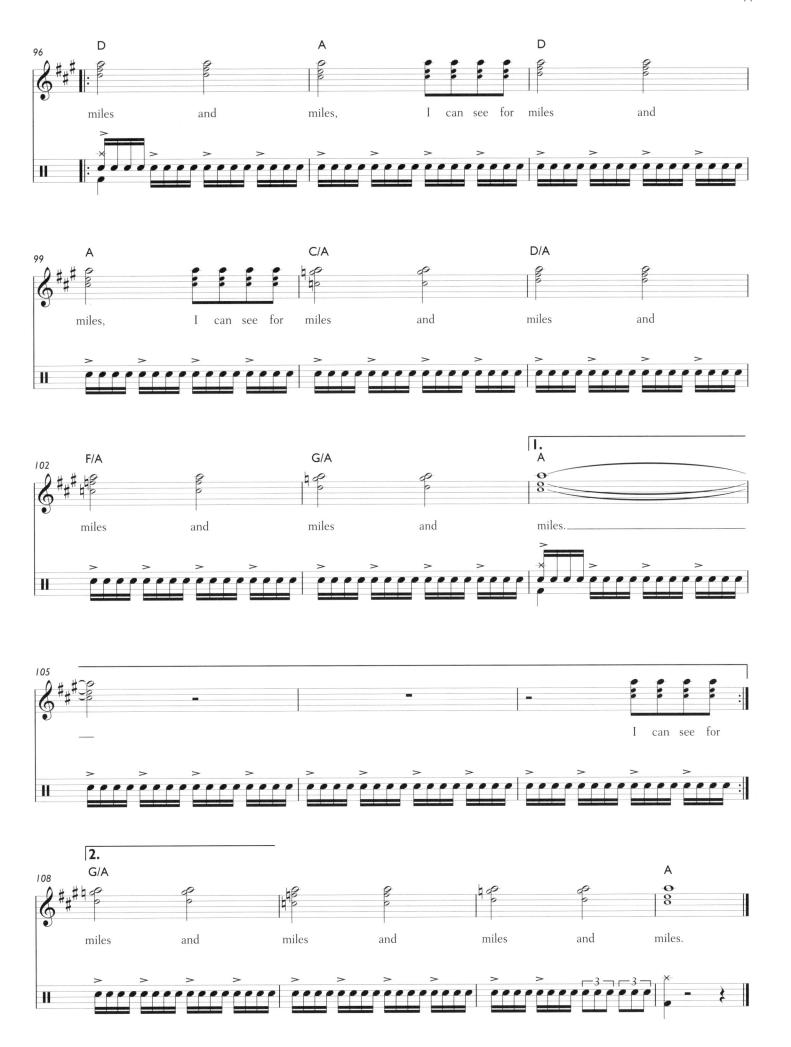

I CAN'T EXPLAIN

Words and Music by Pete Townshend

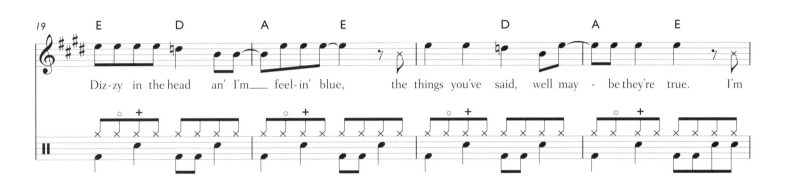

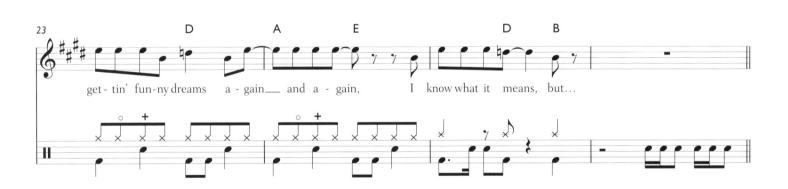

can't ex - plain,   a- yeah,   hear what I say,_ girl.

(Can't ex - plain)   *(can't ex - plain.)*

(gtr. solo)

Said I can't ex - plain, yeah,   you drive me out-ta my   mind.

Yeah, I'm_ the wor-ry- ing__ kind, babe,   I said I can't ex - plain._____

THE KIDS ARE ALRIGHT

Words and Music by Pete Townshend

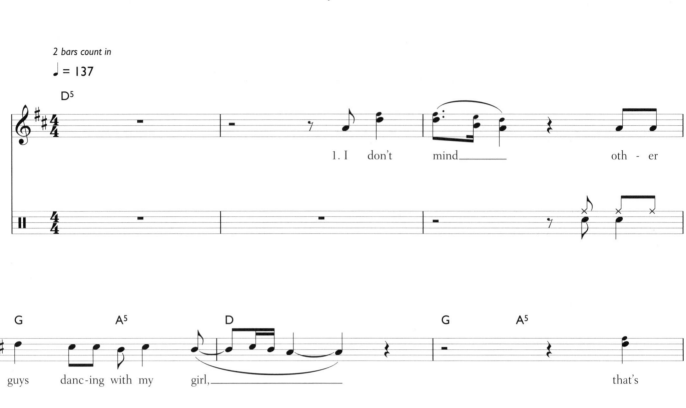

2 bars count in

♩ = 137

1. I don't mind_____ oth - er

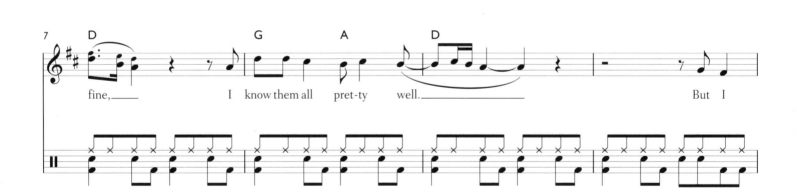

guys danc-ing with my girl,_____ that's fine,_____ I know them all pret-ty well._____ But I

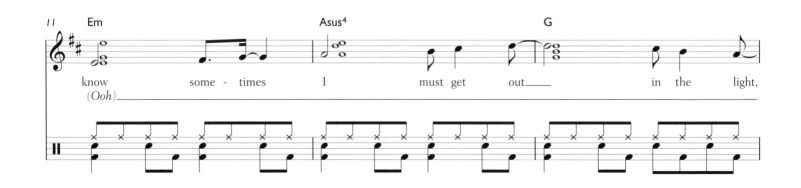

know some - times I must get out_____ in the light,
(Ooh)_____

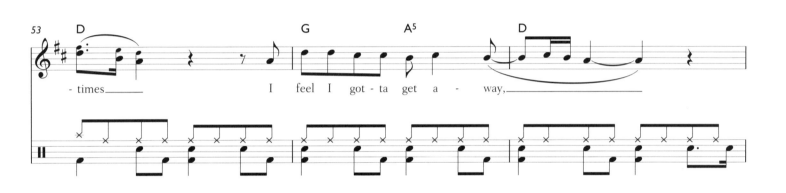

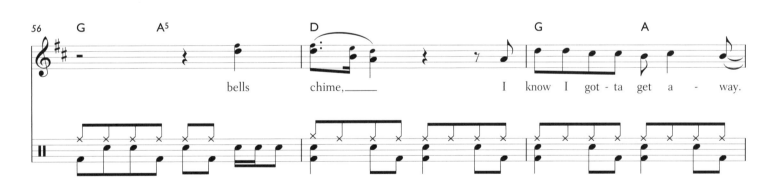

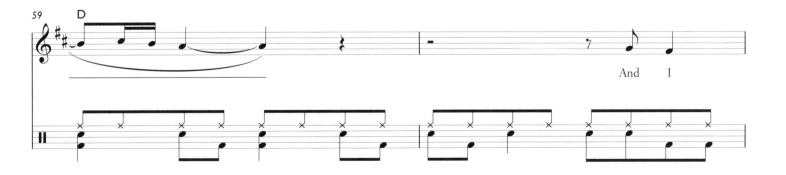

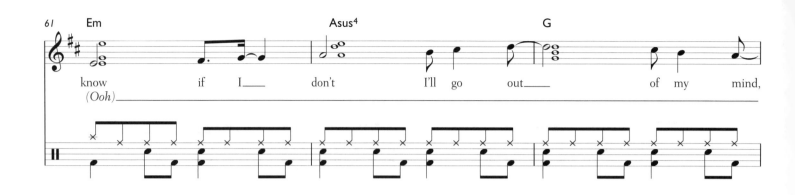

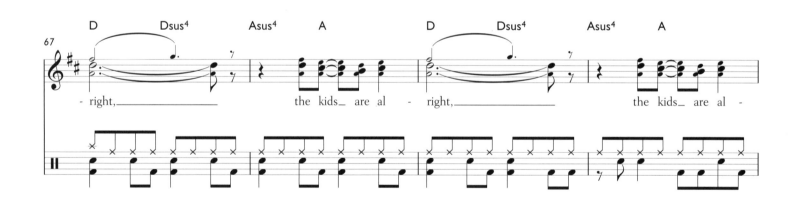

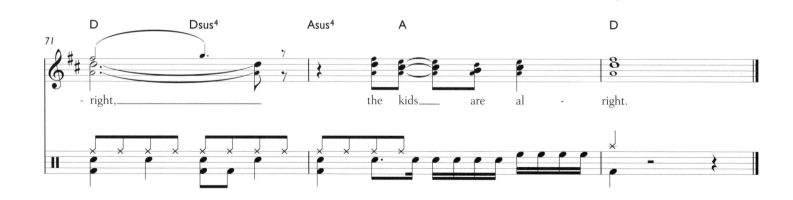

MY GENERATION

Words and Music by Pete Townshend

PICTURES OF LILY

Words and Music by Pete Townshend

PINBALL WIZARD

Words and Music by Pete Townshend

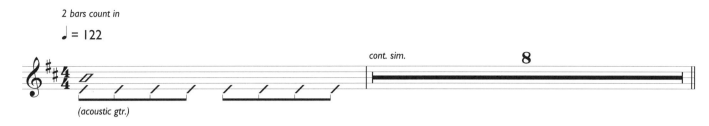

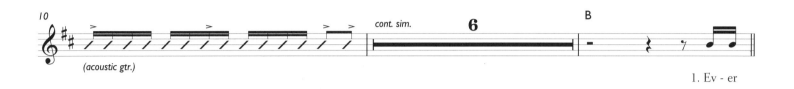

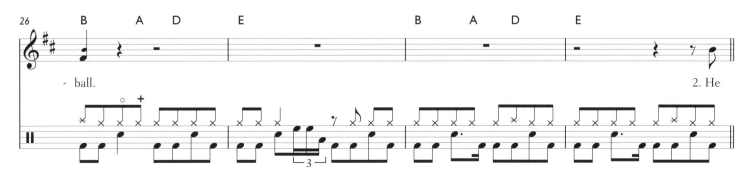

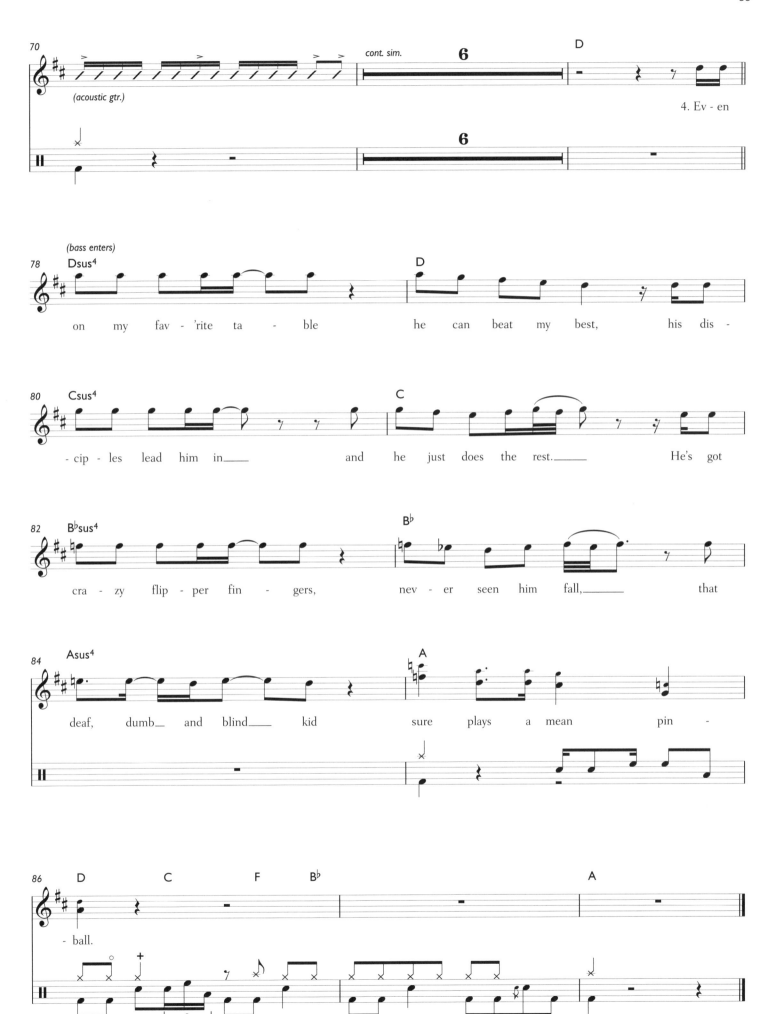

TRACK 13
BACKING TRACK 14

SUBSTITUTE

Words and Music by Pete Townshend

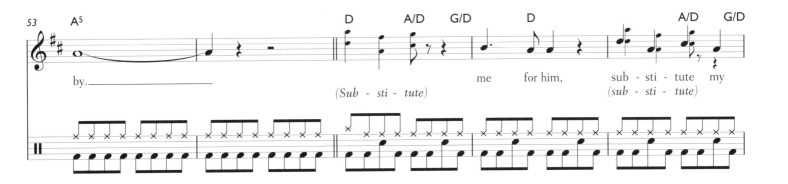

by._____

(Sub - sti - tute)

me   for him,   sub - sti - tute   my
(sub - sti - tute)

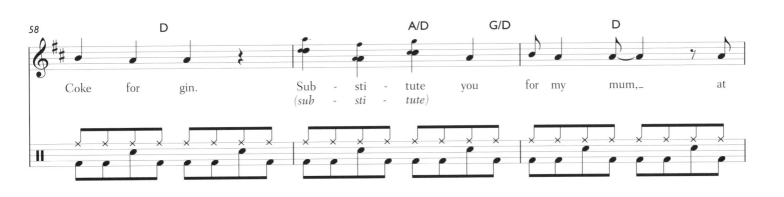

Coke   for   gin.   Sub - sti - tute   you   for my   mum,_   at
(sub - sti - tute)

least   I'll   get   my   wash - ing   done._____
(sub - sti - tute.)

(bass solo)

WON'T GET FOOLED AGAIN

Words and Music by Pete Townshend

D.§ al Coda

2. There's

Coda

Yeah!

Meet the new boss,   same   as the old   boss.

HH (loose)

cymbal roll   choke

DRUM CHARTS

TRACK [1]
BACKING TRACK [2]

I CAN SEE FOR MILES

Words and Music by Pete Townshend

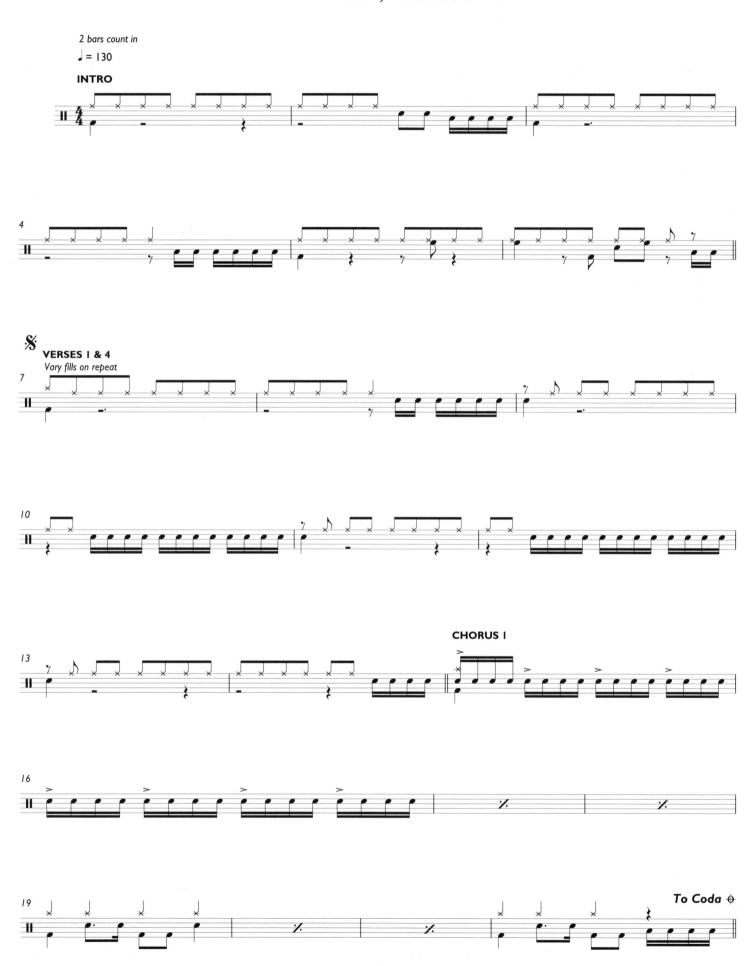

VERSE 2

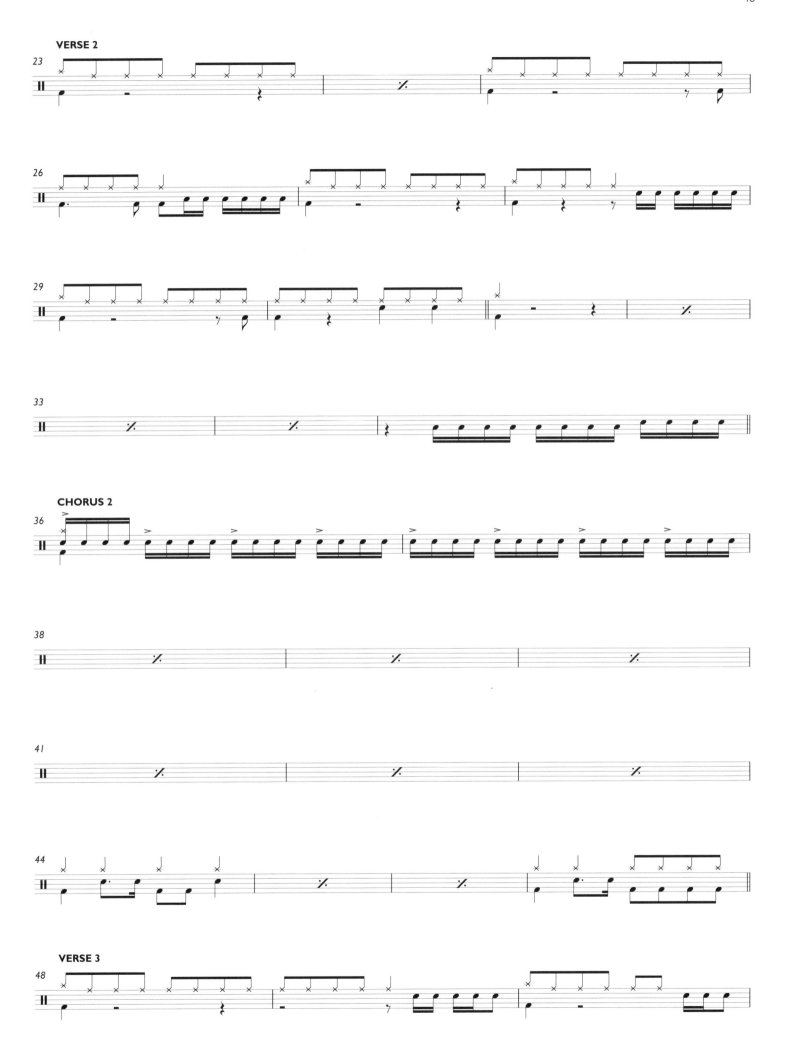

CHORUS 2

VERSE 3

⊕ Coda

VERSE 5

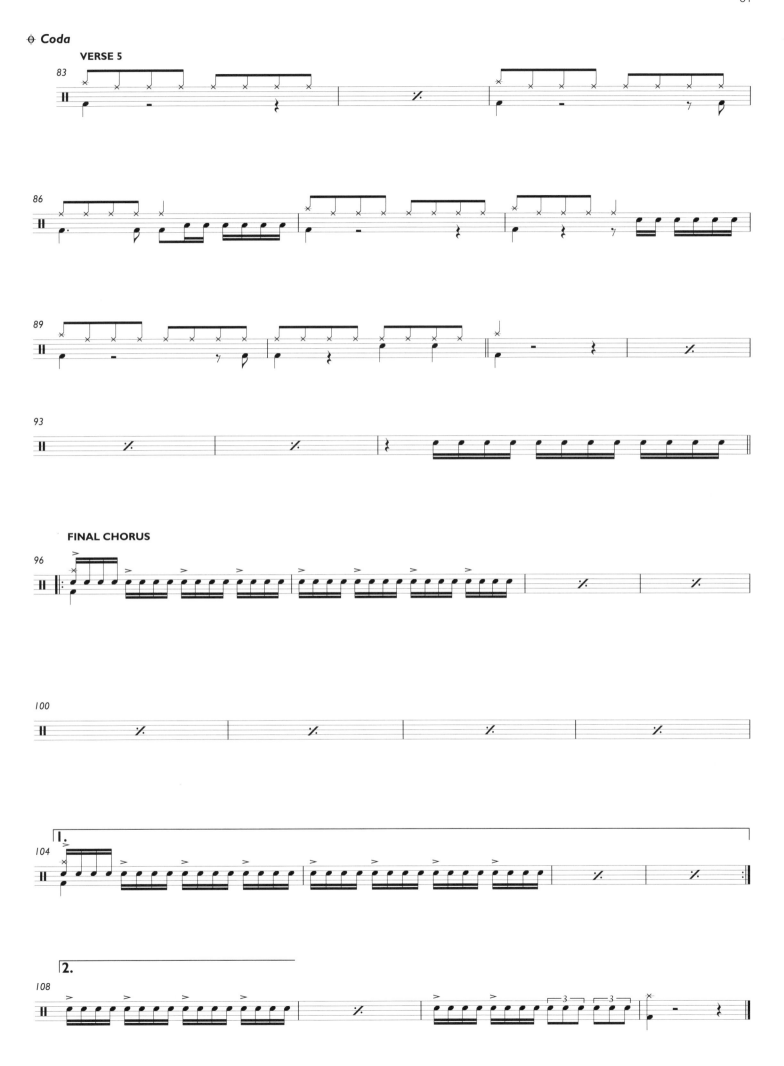

I CAN'T EXPLAIN

Words and Music by Pete Townshend

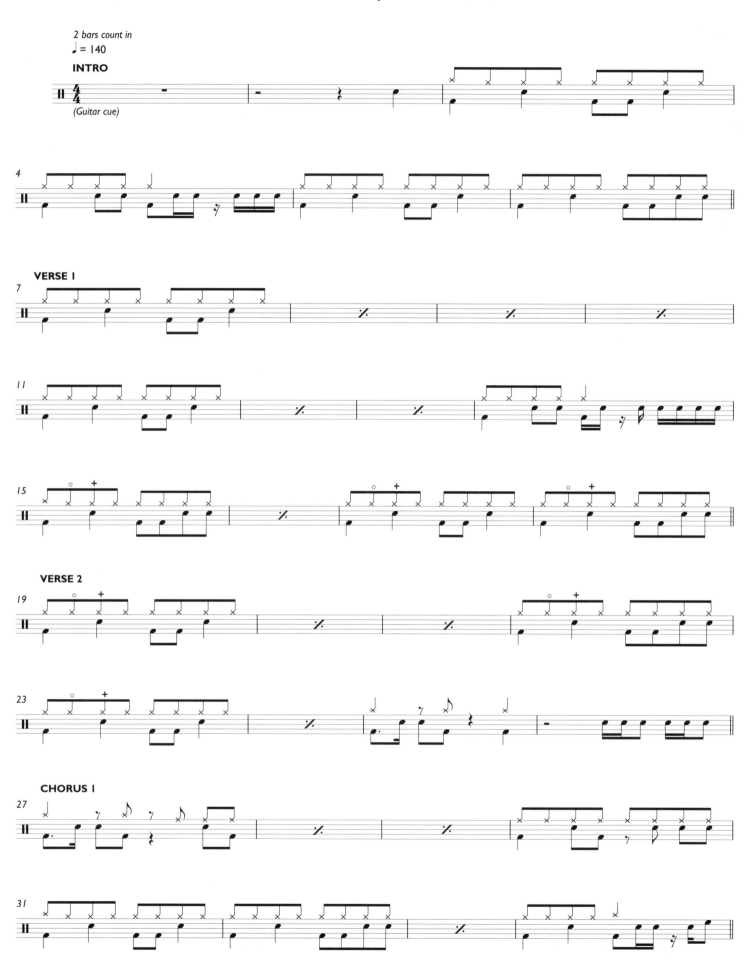

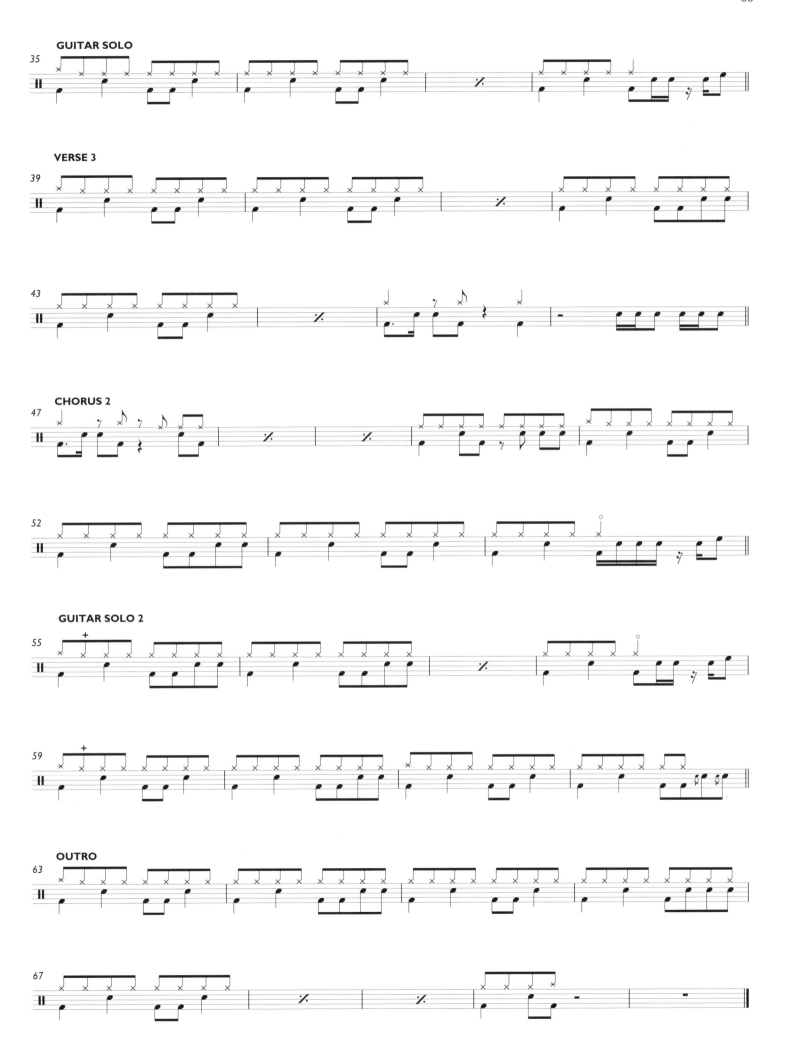

THE KIDS ARE ALRIGHT

Words and Music by Pete Townshend

2 bars count in

♩ = 137

VERSE I

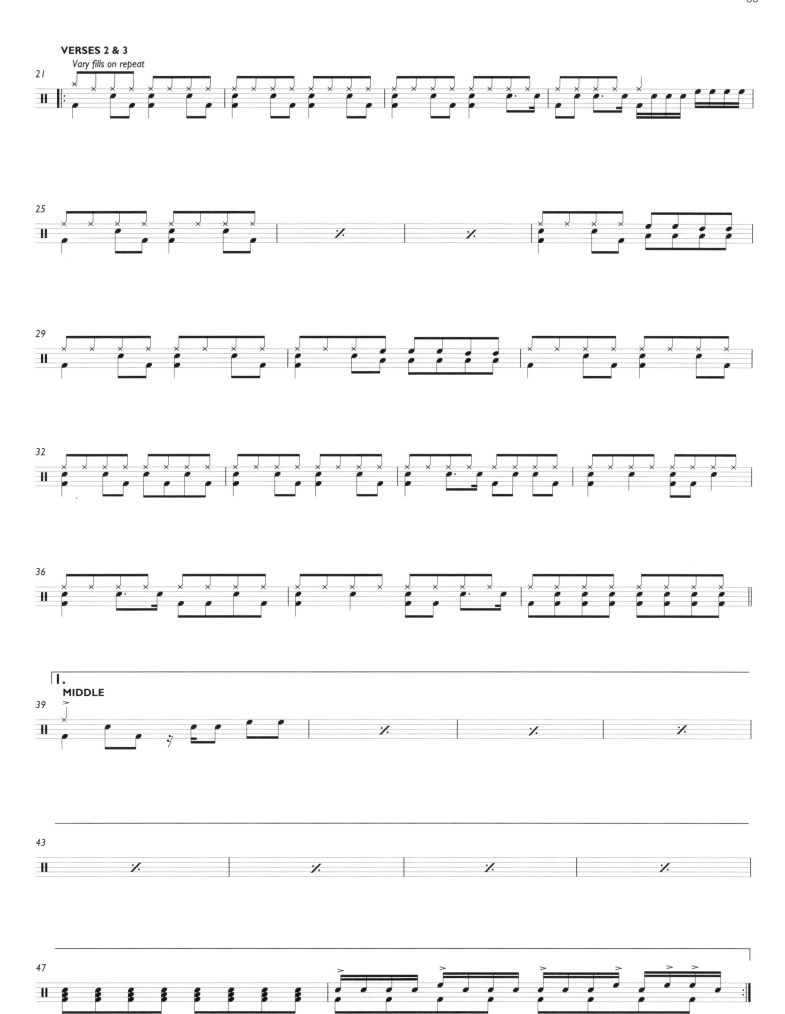

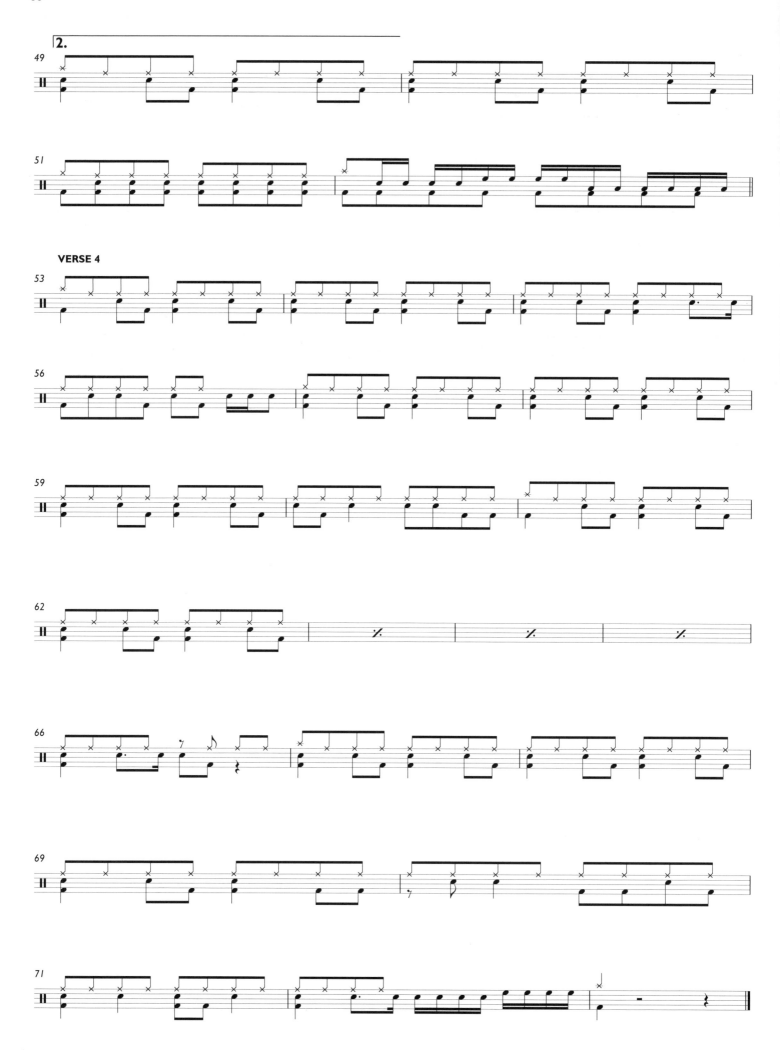

VERSE 4

MY GENERATION

Words and Music by Pete Townshend

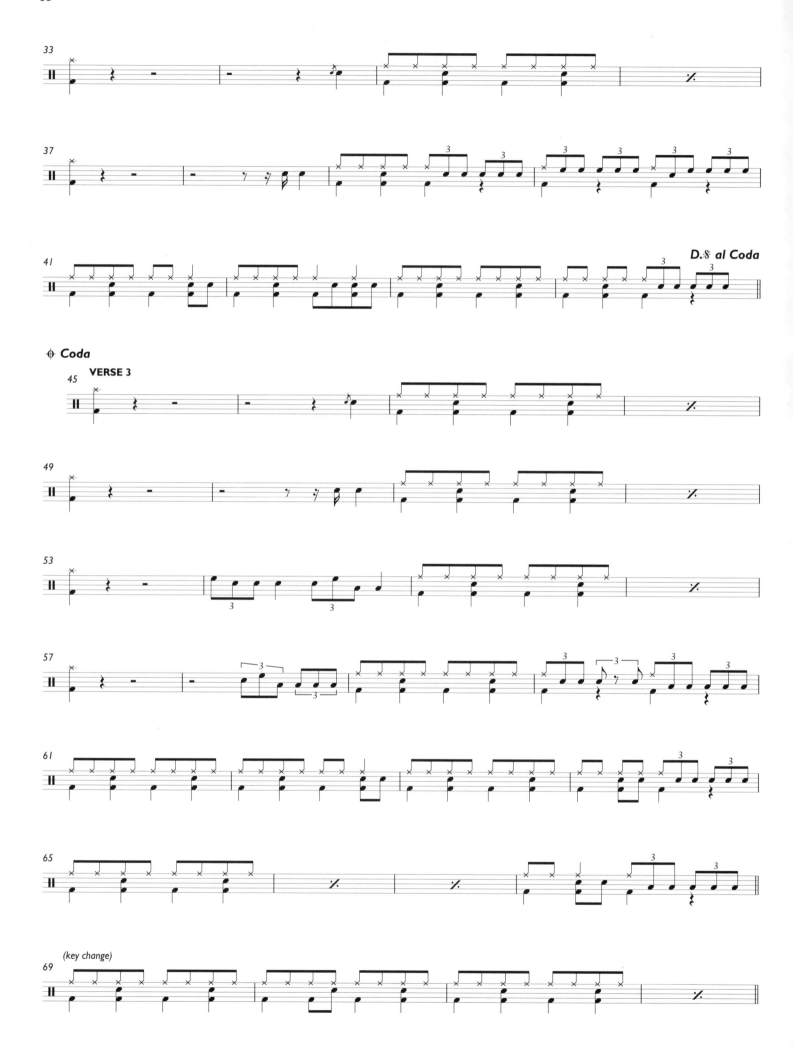

VERSE 4

OUTRO

Vary fills and develop

PICTURES OF LILY

Words and Music by Pete Townshend

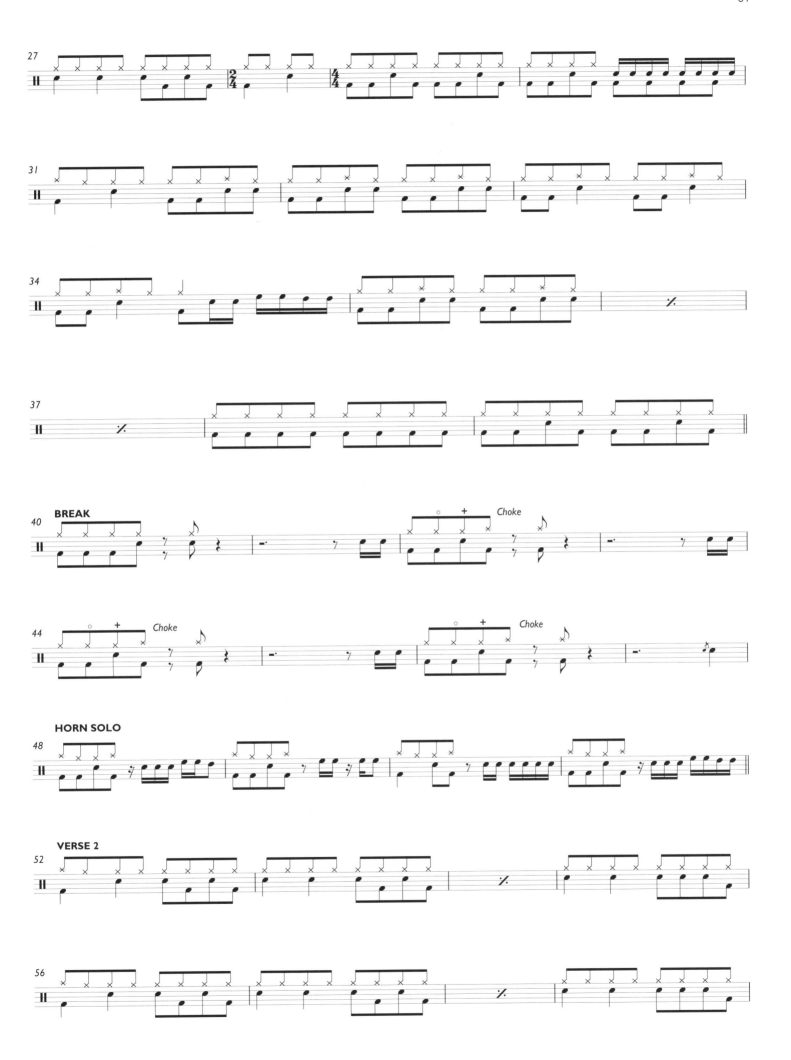

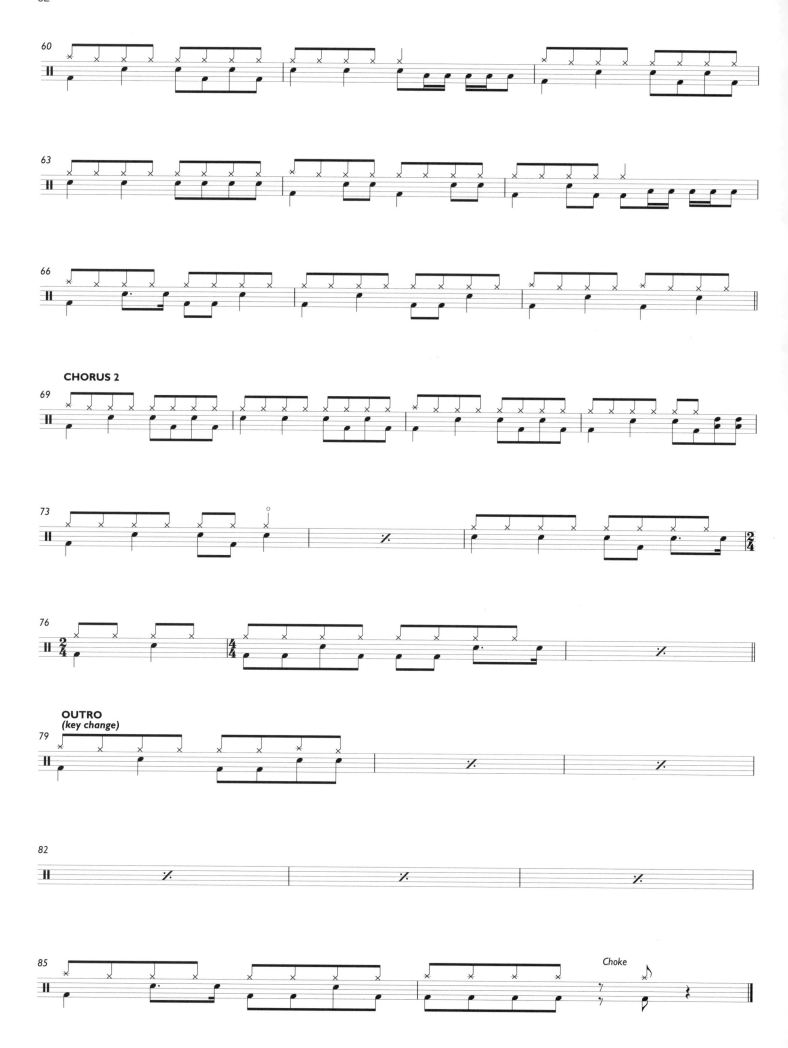

PINBALL WIZARD

Words and Music by Pete Townshend

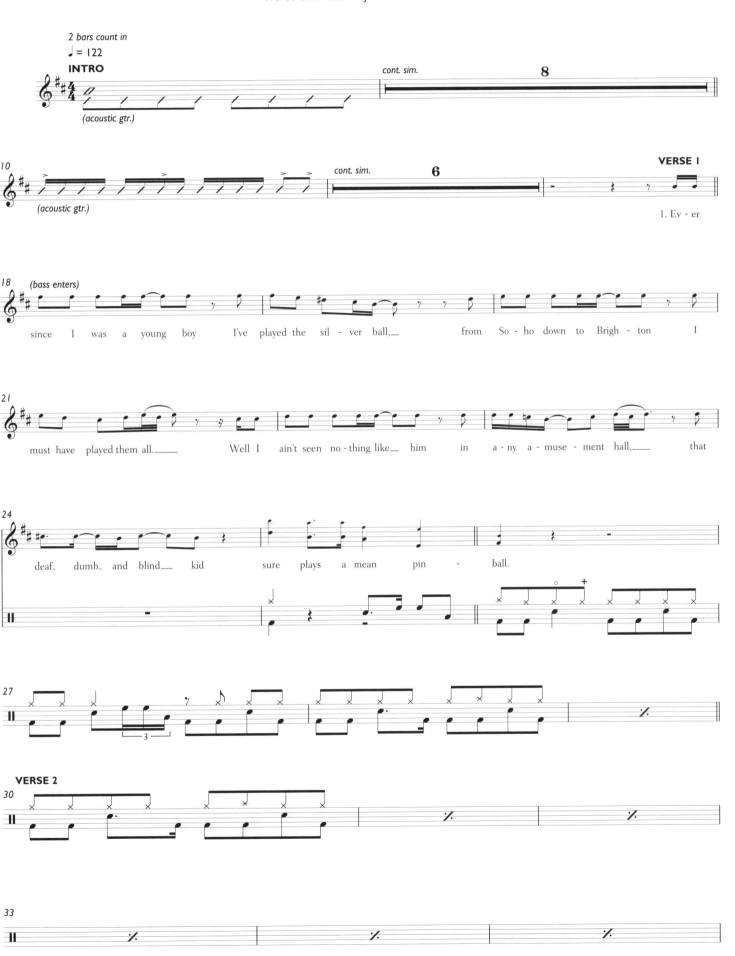

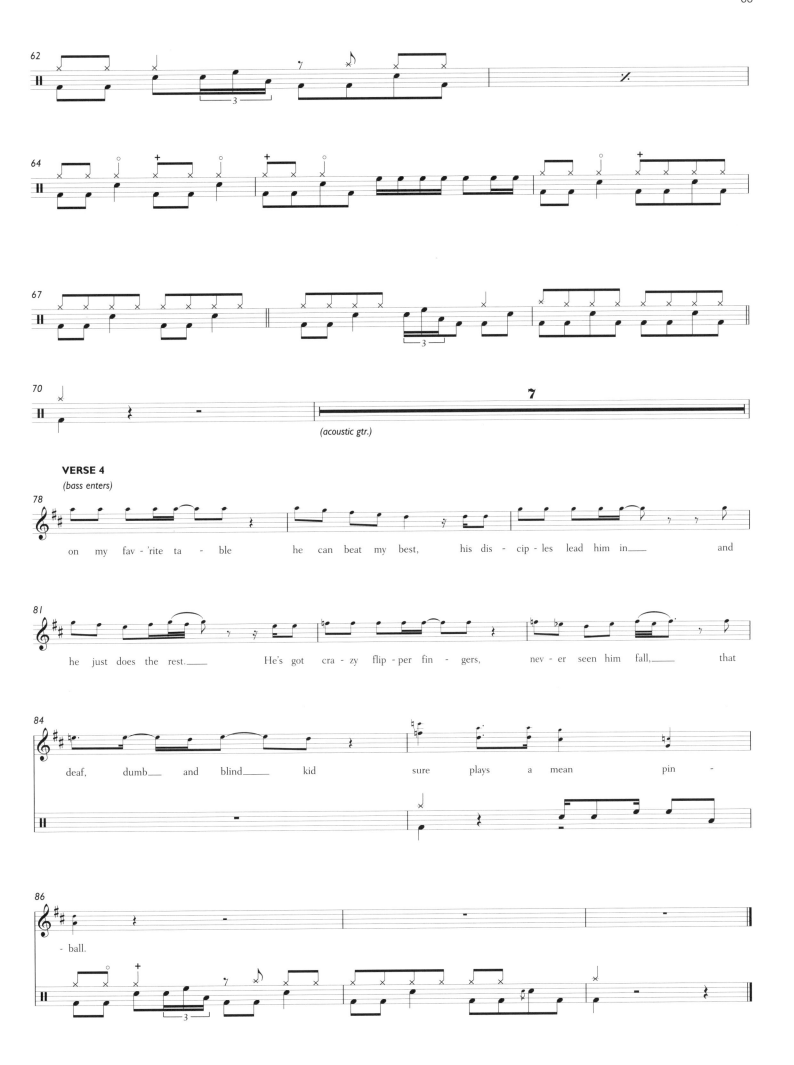

(acoustic gtr.)

VERSE 4

(bass enters)

on my fav-'rite ta - ble   he can beat my best,   his dis - ci - ples lead him in____   and

he just does the rest.____   He's got cra - zy flip - per fin - gers,   nev - er seen him fall,____   that

deaf,   dumb__ and   blind____   kid   sure   plays   a   mean   pin -

- ball.

TRACK 13
BACKING TRACK 14

SUBSTITUTE

Words and Music by Pete Townshend

2 bars count in

♩ = 133

GUITAR RIFF

𝄋 **VERSES 1 & 3**

Vary fills on repeat

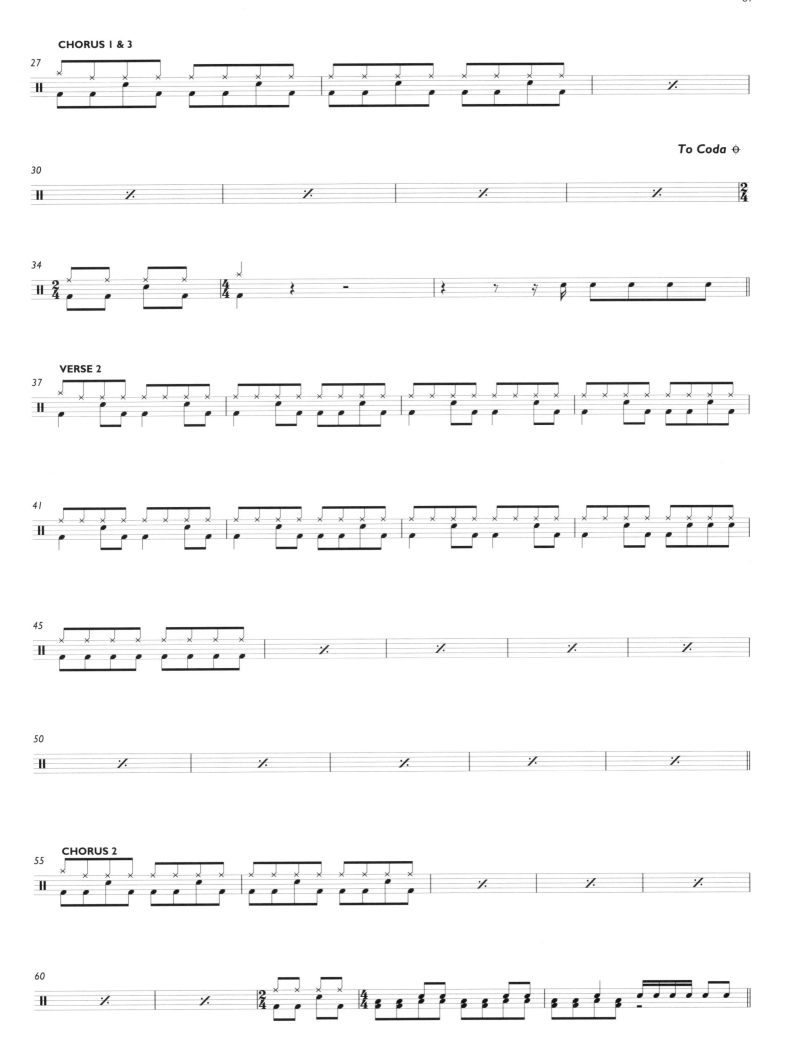

68

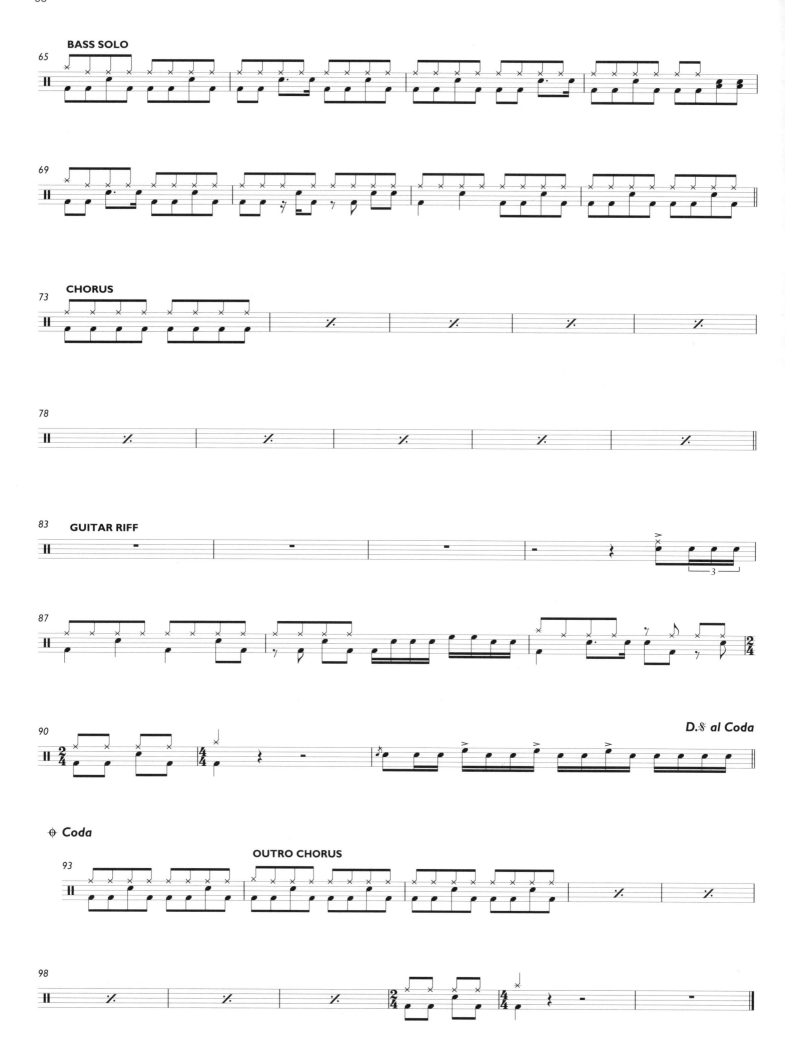

WON'T GET FOOLED AGAIN

Words and Music by Pete Townshend

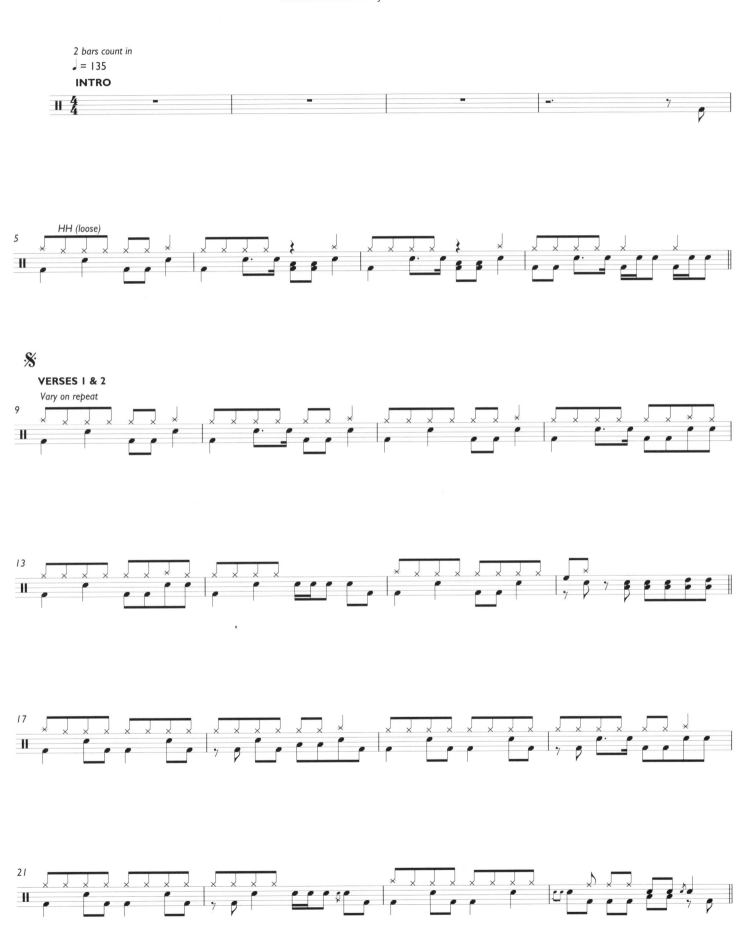

Drum Kit Notation Guide

General notation

Music for drum kit is written on a standard 5-line stave. Mostly you will see a neutral clef, or no clef at the start of each stave, but occasionally bass or treble clefs are used.

Neutral clef   Treble clef   Bass clef

Repeat bars & slash notation

This sign indicates that the previous bar is repeated. Numbered bars are used to help you count through a section.

The two-bar repeat means that the previous two bars are repeated.

Slash notation means "continue in the same style",
with any fills or other changes to to pattern notated as they occur.

Notation for drums

Bass Drum   Snare Drum   Toms: 2-Tom setup   Toms: 3-Tom setup   Toms: 4-Tom setup

Drum techniques

Roll notation
Normally played as a buzz (press) roll - each stick buzzes against the drum head.

Written: Played:

Flam
Two notes very close together, played with different sticks

Flam between two different drums:

Drag
Two grace notes before the beat (played with the same stick) and a main note (with the other stick)

Larger grace-note groups, e.g.:

r r L
l l R   (R = play note with the right-hand stick; L = play with the left-hand stick)